Rules and Recipes with a Difference

by Stan Cullimore

G000138260

Contents

Longman

Edinburgh Gate
Harlow, Essex

Rules *for a Perfect Party*

Rule 1 Invite all your friends.

Rule 2 Have lots of food to eat.

Rule 3 Don't invite anyone you don't like.

Rule 4 Play some exciting games.

Rule 5 Have lots of food to eat.

Rule 6 Play some good music.

Rule 7 Make sure your friends have a good time.

Rule 8 Make sure you have a good time, too.

Rule 9 DON'T FORGET THE FOOD ...

Rule 10 ... AND something to drink!

Recipe for a Perfect Summer Holiday

Ingredients:

1 family

1 car

1 holiday flat

1 seaside

50 litres of petrol

a bag of buckets and spades

some money

lots of fresh air

lots of sunshine

Method:

- Get one family and one bag of buckets and spades.

- Put them in the car.

- Add 50 litres of petrol. (Put it in the petrol tank – NOT in the family.)

- Mix them well by driving for several hours.

- Take the family and buckets and spades out of the car.

- Place them in the holiday flat and let them cool down.

- Show them the seaside.

- Add the fresh air, sunshine and money.

- Now leave them alone for two weeks.

- At the end of this time they will have lots of good memories, suntans ... and a long drive back home!

Rules about Picking Your Nose

Rule 1 DON'T do it at mealtimes.

Rule 2 DON'T do it when you are in the classroom.

Rule 3 DON'T do it when you are watching television.

Rule 4 DON'T do it when you are on the bus.

Rule 5 DON'T do it when you are in a swimming pool.

Rule 6 DON'T do it when you are talking to your friends.

Rule 7 DON'T do it – EVER. Don't you know that it's rude to pick your nose? Use a hanky instead!

Recipe *for a Water Fight*

Ingredients:

1 hot sunny day
some children
some water pistols
lots of water
a change of clothes

Method:

- Wait for a hot sunny day.
- Get your water pistol and fill it with water.
- Go outside.

- Ask one of the other children to come and look at something in the garden.

- When you are both outside, tell the other child that you can see a big drip.

- They will not be able to see it.

- Use your water pistol to squirt them with water.

- Then point at the child and tell them that they are the big drip.

- Wait for the other child to go and get a water pistol.

- Very soon you will be in the middle of a water fight.

- When the fight is over, change your clothes. (If you do not, your mum will tell you off for dripping water all over the house!)

Recipe *for a Mud Pie*

Ingredients:

1 small patch of mud

1 spoon

1 bowl

1 kitchen

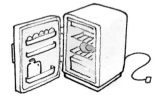

1 fridge

1 small brother (or sister)

1 camera

a little bit of luck

a little bit of work

Method:

- Take the bowl to the small patch of mud.

- Use the spoon to place some mud in the bowl.

- Make the top of the mud smooth – so that it looks like a lovely chocolate pie.

- Take the pie into the kitchen.

- Place the pie in the fridge.

- Tell your small brother (or sister) that there is a chocolate pie in the fridge and they must NOT eat it until teatime.

- Go out of the room.

- With a little bit of luck, your small brother (or sister) will wait until you have gone. Then they will help themselves to a nice big spoonful of mud pie.

- Run back into the room with a camera.

- Take a photo of your brother's (or sister's) face when they taste the mud.

- Run!

Rules to Keep Your Dog Happy

(especially if there is a cat in the house)

Rule 1 Collect up all the cat food in the house and place it in a bag.

Rule 2 Take the cat food back to the shop and change it for large amounts of lovely dog food.

Rule 3 When the cat gets hungry and tries to eat some of the dog's food say, "Bad cat – that food is for dogs only. Don't you know that cats eat smelly socks?"

Rule 4 Whenever you see the cat lying happily on a chair, pick it up and say, "Bad cat – don't you know that this chair is only for dogs?"

Rule 5 Every day you must say to your dog: "You are so much nicer than that stupid, smelly cat. Who likes cats anyway? They are rubbish."

Rules *to Keep Your Cat Happy*

(especially if there is a dog in the house)

Rule 1 Collect up all the dog food in the house and place it in a bag.

Rule 2 Take the dog food back to the shop and change it for large amounts of lovely cat food.

Rule 3 When the dog gets hungry and tries to eat some of the cat's food say, "Bad dog – that food is for cats only. Don't you know that dogs eat smelly socks?"

Rule 4 Whenever you see the dog lying happily on a chair, pick it up and say, "Bad dog – don't you know that this chair is only for cats?"

Rule 5 Every day you must say to your cat: "You are so much nicer than that stupid, smelly dog. Who likes dogs anyway? They are rubbish."

Recipe *for a Pocket Money Rise*

Ingredients:

1 parent

1 morning

1 bed

1 kitchen

breakfast things

a little bit of work

1 tray

at least 1 good reason why
you need more pocket money

a pinch of good luck

Method:

- One morning, after the parent has woken up – and before
  the parent has got out of bed – go into the kitchen.

- Rush round using the breakfast things to make a really nice
  breakfast. (NB: Always remember to make a nice hot cup of
  tea or coffee – this is most important. All parents love their
  children to bring them a nice hot cup of tea or coffee in bed.)

- Place the really nice breakfast on the tray and take it to
  the parent.

- Wait until the parent is happily munching away on their
  breakfast and drinking their nice hot cup of tea or coffee.
  Start talking about the weather / the dog / knitting / the
  old days / anything else the parent likes to talk about.

After a few minutes of boring conversation, mention the good reason why you need more pocket money. For example: you are saving up to take your gran on holiday or you want to buy the parent a really nice present. (NB: This reason does not have to be true – it just has to sound like a good reason to give you more pocket money. After all, parents never really listen to anything you say.)

Now, if you add a pinch of good luck, the parent should nod happily and say that they will give you more pocket money because you are such a kind and thoughtful child.

Now tiptoe out of the room and leave the parent to go back to sleep.

⚠ SAFETY WARNING!

Be careful – the parent may know the rules for parents which include:

Always ask yourself, "WHY is my child bringing me breakfast in bed?"

Listen to EVERY word your child says.

Rules to Keep on the Right Side of Your Teacher

Rule 1 Do all your homework every evening.

Rule 2 Go to bed nice and early so that you are never tired at school.

Rule 3 Eat a good breakfast every morning so that you don't get hungry in the middle of lessons.

Rule 4 Listen carefully to everything the teacher says.

Rule 5 Never talk to your friends when the teacher is talking.

Rule 6 Never talk to your friends when you should be working.

Rule 7 When you leave school in the afternoon, always thank your teacher for helping you to learn new and interesting things. (Well, at least say goodbye!)

17

Rules to Keep on the Wrong *Side of Your Teacher*

Rule 1 Don't bother doing your homework. Spend the time making up excuses as to why you couldn't do it.

Rule 2 Stay up late and watch television all night. That way you can sleep all day at school.

Rule 3 Don't eat breakfast before you go to school. Take a packed lunch and eat it when you get hungry in the middle of lessons.

Rule 4 Never listen to anything the teacher says.

Rule 5 Always talk to your friends when the teacher is talking.

Rule 6 Always talk to your friends when you should be working.

Rule 7 When you leave school in the afternoon, tell your teacher that you don't want to learn anything because you like being stupid.

Rules about Burping in Public

Rule 1 Don't do it when you are at the breakfast table, at lunchtime or teatime.

Rule 2 Don't do it when you are in the classroom, cloakroom or in assembly.

Rule 3 Don't do it when you are watching television with your family, friends or neighbours.

Rule 4 Don't do it when you are on the bus, the train or in the car.

Rule 5 Don't do it when you are in a swimming pool, bowling alley or cinema.

Rule 6 Don't do it when you are talking to your friends – especially your boyfriend or girlfriend.

Rule 7 In fact, don't do it – EVER. Don't you know that it's rude to burp in public?

Recipe *for a Perfect School Day*

Ingredients:

1 school day

a small pinch

Method:

1 Wake up – late. Allow your parents to bring you breakfast in bed. Lie in bed and watch television for a few hours. Get up eventually and dress.

2 Get a taxi to the park to hang out with your friends. Buy several ice creams and eat them.

3 Return home to play a few computer games. Order
   a takeaway pizza for tea. Spend the evening watching
   videos and texting your friends. Finally, go to bed.

4 Now, pinch yourself and wake up! Remember – you are
   a child; you HAVE to go to school!

PINCH!

PINCH!

Rules *to Keep Your Bedroom Looking Tidy**

(*After all, if your bedroom looks untidy, someone will shout at you to tidy it up.)

Rule 1 If you have any dirty, smelly clothes that need washing, throw them under the bed and out of sight. Otherwise they will sit in the corner looking messy.

Rule 2 If you have any rubbish, don't throw it in the rubbish bin because it will make the rubbish bin look horrible. Instead, throw it under your bed.

Rule 3 If you have any food in your room, eat what you
want and then throw the rest under your bed
before it starts to look and smell disgusting.

Rule 4 If you have any games, CDs or magazines lying around
making the room look untidy, throw them under your bed.

Rule 5 One day your bed will have so much stuff under it that
you won't be able to climb into it any more. When this
happens, pull everything out from under your bed.
Then go and tell someone that your dog / cat / goldfish
/ brother / sister / invisible friend (you choose which
one) has made your room all messy. Burst into tears
and say that someone else will have to tidy it up
because you are too upset to manage it.

Rules to Make You Rich

Always make sure that you spend less money than you earn.

Rules to Make You Poor

Always make sure that you spend lots more money than you earn.

Recipe *for World Peace*

Ingredients:

1 Earth
1 human race
1 pinch of hope

Method:

1 Take the human race and remove all greed.

2 Remove all racism, sexism and intolerance.

3 Place the human race on the face of the Earth. Allow them to live and love, wherever and whoever they wish. Allow them to worship the god of their choice.

4 Take one pinch of hope and leave the mix to settle.

5 Serve.

Recipe *for a Long and Happy Life*

Ingredients:

1 family
1 bunch of friends
good health

Method:

- Put the family in a nice, warm place – home is perfect for this. Now stay with the family for years and years – adding friends as time goes by.

- Wait until you are old enough and ready to leave the family home. Now it is time for you and your friends to go off and explore the world and learn about life. After a few years you will start to feel all grown-up. This is the perfect time to begin thinking about starting a family of your own.

- Keep on living and enjoy life to the full.

  NB: Throughout the above, you need to keep your good health – never forget to be grateful if you can stay healthy!

Rules *for Dealing with Aliens*

Rule 1 When you first meet aliens, remember that they have come from another planet. This means that they have travelled many millions of miles through space to be here on Earth. Bear in mind the fact that humans haven't worked out how to travel millions of miles through space yet!

WELCOME

Rule 2 This means that these aliens must be clever. Very clever! So be polite when you talk to them.

Rule 3 If they listen to what you say and then reply in a language that you can understand – be careful. Be very careful!

ESARHP KOOB

HOW ARE YOU?   SPLIG BURT GARF?

WHO ARE YOU   NOIK BURT GA

BUZZ OFF

GET LOST

Rule 4 This is *very*, VERY important. Whatever you do – DON'T ANNOY THESE ALIENS. After all, if they are so clever that they can travel through space and speak to humans – they are probably clever enough to have thought up a way of exterminating people that they don't like!!!

OME PEACE

Recipe *for Keeping Your Friends*

Ingredients:

a pinch of patience

a touch of tolerance

a measure of kindness

a teaspoon of truth

a sprinkle of apologies

Method:

- Take one measure of kindness, remembering to use the same amount as you would like to have used on you.

- Add a pinch of patience – especially when your friends are going on about something that you find boring.

- Stir in a touch of tolerance – everyone has the right to their own opinions.

- Add a teaspoon of truth, bearing in mind that too much can be harmful!

- Mix well and leave to stand.

- Serve with a sprinkle of apologies whenever they are needed.